TEST SUCCESS

Targeting the
CTB-TerraNova
Reading and Language Arts • Mathematics

Harcourt Achieve

Rigby • Steck-Vaughn

www.HarcourtAchieve.com
1.800.531.5015

Harcourt Achieve Inc. is indebted to the following for permission to use material in this book:

page 14: "Comfortable Old Chair" from *Dogs and Dragons, Trees and Dreams* by Karla Kuskin. Copyright © 1992 by Karla Kuskin. Reprinted by permission of Scott Treimel New York.

page 22: "How to Care for a Pet" (retitled "How to Get a Dog"), from *How to Eat Like a Child* by Delia Ephron. Reprinted by permission of International Creative Management, Inc. Copyright © 1977, 1978 by Delia Ephron.

page 41: "The Green Chicken" by Alvin Schwartz. Copyright © 1992 by Alvin Schwartz. Published in STORIES TO TELL A CAT; published by HarperCollins. Reprinted by permission of Curtis Brown, Ltd.

Photo Credits:

p. 34 © Mike Powell/Allsport; pp. 36, 55 © AP/Wide World Photos; p. 56 © Doug Bensinger/Allsport; p. 62 © AP/WorldWide Photos.

ISBN: 0-7398-9751-9

Printed in the United States of America.

5 6 7 8 9 2266 14
4500513039

Targeting the
CTB-TerraNova
Grade 3
CONTENTS

Parent Letter..4

SECTION A: READING AND LANGUAGE ARTS
Information 7
    Information about this section of the book.
Reading
    Lesson 1: Reading Comprehension 8
    Reading Review Test..14
Language Arts
    Lesson 2: Sentence Structure..24
    Lesson 3: Writing Strategies 26
    Lesson 4: Editing Skills 28
    Language Arts Review Test 30
Comprehensive Test
    Reading and Language Arts..37
    Part 1 38
    Part 2 54

SECTION B: MATHEMATICS
Information 69
    Information about this section of the book.
Mathematics
    Lesson 1: Number and Number Relations 71
    Lesson 2: Computation and Numerical Estimation 72
    Lesson 3: Operation Concepts 73
    Lesson 4: Measurement 74
    Lesson 5: Geometry and Spatial Sense 75
    Lesson 6: Data Analysis, Statistics, and Probability 76
    Lesson 7: Patterns, Functions, and Algebra 77
    Lesson 8: Problem Solving and Reasoning 78
    Lesson 9: Communication 79
    Mathematics Review Test..80
Comprehensive Test
    Mathematics 87
    Part 1 88
    Part 2 90

ANSWER KEY 101
    Answers are provided to all the questions and problems in the book.

Dear Parent or Educator,

Welcome to **Targeting the CTB-TerraNova**. You have selected a book that will help your child develop the skills he or she needs to succeed on the CTB-TerraNova.

Although testing can be a source of anxiety for children, this book will give your child the preparation and practice that he or she needs to feel better prepared and more confident when taking the CTB-TerraNova. Research shows that children who are acquainted with the scoring format of standardized tests score higher on those tests. Students also score higher when they practice and understand the skills and objectives covered on the test.

This book has many features that will help you prepare your child to take the CTB-TerraNova:

- Lessons for the child about how to answer test questions and hints to guide the child toward the correct response
- Test-taking tips
- Tests that simulate the actual CTB-TerraNova tests
- A complete answer key

If your child expresses anxiety about taking a test or completing these lessons, help him or her understand what causes the stress. Then, talk about ways to eliminate anxiety. Above all, enjoy this time you spend with your child. He or she will feel your support, and test scores will improve as success in test taking is experienced.

Help your child maintain a positive attitude about taking a standardized test such as the CTB-TerraNova. Let your child know that each test provides an opportunity to shine.

Sincerely,

The Educators and Staff of
Harcourt School Supply

P.S. You might want to visit our website at www.HarcourtSchoolSupply.com for more test preparation materials as well as additional review of content areas.

Section
A

Reading and Language Arts

About Section A: Reading and Language Arts

This section of the book has been developed to refresh basic skills, familiarize your child with test formats and directions, and teach test-taking strategies. This section of the book is divided into three components: Lessons, Review Tests, and Comprehensive Test.

Lessons

There are lessons on reading comprehension and language arts skills assessed on the CTB-TerraNova Reading and Language Arts test. Each lesson contains:

- *Try This:* a skill strategy that enables your child to approach each lesson in a logical manner
- *Sample:* to familiarize your child with test-taking items
- *Think It Through:* the correct answer to the sample item and an explanation that tells why the correct answer is correct and why the incorrect answers are wrong
- several practice questions based on the lesson and modeled on the kinds of items found on the CTB-TerraNova

Review Test

The lessons are followed by a short Review Test that covers all the skills in the lessons. This test is designed to provide your child with independent practice that will familiarize him or her with the testing situation.

Comprehensive Test

The last component in this section is a Comprehensive Test. This test gives your child an opportunity to take a test under conditions that parallel those he or she will face when taking the CTB-TerraNova Reading and Language Arts test.

In order to simulate the CTB-TerraNova test as closely as possible, we have suggested time limits for the Comprehensive Test. This will enable your child to experience test taking under the same structured conditions that apply when achievement tests are administered. Furthermore, your child will have a final opportunity to apply the skills he or she has learned in this section prior to taking the CTB-TerraNova.

The recommended time limits are:
Part 1: 40 minutes
Part 2: 60 minutes

Answer Key

The Answer Key at the back of the book contains the answers for all the questions found in this section.

Reading

Directions: Read each story carefully. Then read each question. Darken the circle for the correct answer.

 More than one answer may seem correct. Choose the answer that goes best with the story.

Sample A

Making Breakfast

Dad and I made our own breakfast. We made pancakes. They tasted better than Mom's pancakes. Dad and I decided we would keep this as our little secret.

Why will they keep the secret?

○ They do not want Mom to know they cooked breakfast.

◉ They do not want to hurt Mom's feelings.

○ They burned the pancakes.

 The correct answer is <u>They do not want to hurt Mom's feelings.</u> The story states that the pancakes tasted better than Mom's pancakes. But they will keep this secret. If they tell Mom they might hurt her feelings.

 More than one answer may seem correct. Choose the answer that goes best with the story.

Sample B

Vera and Kit

Vera and Kit were playing. Kit ran to hide. Vera looked for her. Then it began to rain. Vera and Kit got wet. They ran to the house.

What were the girls doing?

○ playing football

○ playing hopscotch

◉ playing hide-and-seek

 The correct answer is <u>playing hide-and-seek</u>. The story states that Kit ran to hide. Then Vera looked for her. This is not how to play football. This is not how to play hopscotch.

8

Directions: Here is a story about a girl named Ava and her donkey. Read this story carefully. Then read each question. Darken the circle for the correct answer.

Ava and Sam

Ava lived in the mountains with her family and a donkey named Sam. Ava and Sam went everywhere together. Sam was a good mountain climber. Ava was not as good at climbing. She had to watch where she walked. When the path was dangerous, Ava would ride on Sam's back. Sam never slipped or fell. He was always careful when Ava was on his back.

Ava rode the donkey on the path down to the stream. There were fish swimming in the stream. Ava and the donkey splashed in the cool, clear water. Later, when they returned home, Ava gave Sam a pail of the food he likes. She brushed his back. Then, Ava went inside for dinner.

Go

1 Where did Ava and Sam live?

- ○ on a farm
- ◉ in the mountains
- ○ in the city

2 Why did Ava ride the donkey to the stream?

- ○ The donkey was tired.
- ○ The path was long.
- ◉ The path was dangerous.

3 How do you know Ava loves Sam?

- ○ She splashes in the water with him.
- ◉ She feeds him the food he likes.
- ○ She rides on his back.

4 Find the picture of Ava and Sam.

5 If Sam became sick, what would Ava probably do?

- ○ She would go to the stream alone.
- ○ She would find another donkey.
- ◉ She would take care of him.

6 He was always <u>careful</u> when Ava was on his back.

A word that means the opposite of <u>careful</u> is

- ◉ careless
- ○ slow
- ○ watchful

Directions: Read this poem about two kittens carefully. Then read each question. Darken the circle for the correct answer.

TWO LITTLE KITTENS

Two little kittens, one stormy night,
    Began to hiss, and then to fight;
One had a mouse, the other had none,
    And that's the way the fight begun.

"I'll have that mouse," said the biggest cat;
    "You'll have that mouse? We'll see about that!"
"I'll have that mouse," said the oldest son;
    "You won't have the mouse," said the little one.

I told you before it was a stormy night,
    When these two little kittens began to fight;
The old woman grabbed her sweeping broom,
    And swept the two kittens right out of the room.

The ground was covered with ice and snow,
    And the two little kittens had nowhere to go;
So they laid themselves down on the mat at the door,
    While the old woman finished sweeping the floor.

Then they crept in, as quiet as mice,
    All wet with snow, and cold as ice,
For they found it was better, that stormy night,
    To lie down and sleep than to hiss and fight.

7 **Why were the two kittens fighting?**

● They did not want to share the mouse.

○ One kitten wanted to let the mouse go.

○ They did not like each other.

○ One kitten wanted to sleep alone.

8 **Why does the old woman sweep the kittens outside?**

● She does not want them to fight.

○ She is cleaning the house.

○ They do not belong in the house.

○ They sleep on the mat at the door.

9 **What lesson did the kittens learn?**

○ You should be quiet.

○ You should go to sleep.

● You should not fight.

○ You should not eat mice.

10 **What most likely happened to the mouse?**

○ The biggest cat got it.

● It ran away when the kittens started to fight.

○ The littlest cat got it.

○ It crept into the house with the kittens.

Directions: Read the story carefully. Then read the question. Darken the circle for the correct answer.

Sample A

Celina's Vacation Plans

Celina is excited about going camping with her family this summer. They plan to go to the Grand Canyon where they will stay for two weeks.

How long will Celina's family camp?

- ○ two days
- ◉ two weeks
- ○ the entire summer

Directions: Here is a poem about a place to rest. Read this poem. Then read each question. Darken the circle for the correct answer.

Comfortable Old Chair

by Karla Kuskin

A bird has a nest
　A fox has a lair
A den is home
　If you're a bear.
I have a comfortable old chair.

Soft pillowed blue,
　a flowered cloud.
The perfect place to read aloud
　to myself or silently
letting long words run over me,
　letting the stories I have read
make moving pictures in my head.
　New chairs are nice
but mine is best.

My spot to think in
brood in
rest
to plot in
dream in, many dreams,
to scheme a few outlandish schemes in.
Kings need crowns to be the king
but me
I can be anything
any person
anywhere
if I just have my book and chair.

brood = worry

plot = plan

scheme = plan

---

1   What does a bear call home?

2 **How does the poet feel when she's in her chair?**

- ○ unhappy
- ◉ at home
- ○ lonely

3 **The poet wrote**

**letting the stories I have read
make <u>moving pictures</u> in my head.**

What are the <u>moving pictures</u>?

- ○ movies
- ◉ books
- ○ thoughts

4 **What kind of person is the poet?**

- ◉ a dreamer
- ○ a king
- ○ a lazy person

5 **What would happen if the poet's chair ripped?**

- ○ She would buy a new one.
- ○ She would throw it out.
- ◉ She would fix the rip.

Directions: Here is a tale about a boy and two giants. Read this tale. Then read each question. Darken the circle for the correct answer.

Sammy Small and the Giants

Sammy Small's mother was leaving the house. "Now," she directed her son, "don't leave the house."

"Why not?" Sammy asked.

"The giant Sneezy Snatcher will grab you," said his mother.

Sammy didn't believe in Sneezy Snatcher. So, as soon as his mother left the house, Sammy left too.

But Sneezy Snatcher was real. And just then he was standing by Sammy's house with a sack over his shoulder. Sneezy picked Sammy up with just two fingers. Sammy squealed and squirmed, but it did no good. Sneezy Snatcher dropped him into the sack.

When Sneezy got home, he called his wife, who was also a giant. "Look love," he said. "I caught a boy we can have for dinner. You watch him while I go out and get a few vegetables to put in the pot with him."

After Sneezy left, Sammy sat on the table looking at Mrs. Snatcher. She looked so silly that Sammy began to build up his courage. "Does Mr. Snatcher ever eat anything but boys?" he finally asked. "Does he sometimes have pudding for dessert?"

"Sneezy and I just love pudding," Mrs. Snatcher said. "But we don't have it often. These are bad times for us giants."

"My mom made a great big pudding this morning," Sammy said. "It's got lots of raisins in it."

"Mmmm," said Mrs. Snatcher. "That sounds delicious."

"I know Mom would be happy to give you some," said Sammy. "Shall I run home and get some from her?"

"You are a generous boy," said Mrs. Snatcher. "By all means, go home. But be sure to hurry back because I'll need time to boil you for dinner."

"I'll be as fast as lightning," Sammy promised. And he did run home as fast as lightning. But you can be sure that he didn't go back to be boiled. Sammy lived happily ever after because he never went out of the house without his mother again.

6 **Why was Sammy caught by the giant?**

- ○ He didn't listen to his mother.
- ○ He was good to eat.
- ● He stole the pudding for dessert.

7 **Why was Sneezy Snatcher able to pick Sammy up with just two fingers?**

- ● Sammy was a little boy.
- ○ Sneezy Snatcher was huge.
- ○ Sammy didn't fight back.

8 **How does Sammy feel at the end of the tale?**

9 **How do we know that Mrs. Snatcher wasn't too smart?**

- ○ She liked pudding for dessert.
- ○ She looked silly.
- ● She let Sammy go home to get the pudding.

Directions: Here is a story about a famous American. Read the story. Then read each question. Darken the circle for the correct answer.

Johnny Appleseed

The next time you bite into a crisp, red, juicy apple, remember the name John Chapman. John Chapman, perhaps better known as Johnny Appleseed, planted many apple trees in early America.

Johnny was born in Massachusetts during the Revolutionary War. When he grew up, he traveled west. He planted apple trees wherever he went. Johnny helped the new settlers who were moving to the West during this time. He gave apple seeds and young apple trees to them.

Johnny was well-liked because of all his good deeds. He made friends with both settlers and Native Americans. Many stories, poems, and plays have been written about him. It is said that he had a pet wolf and slept in a treetop. We don't know how many of these stories are true. But we do know that Johnny Appleseed helped many people.

10 Why is John Chapman better known as Johnny Appleseed?

○ The name Appleseed tells you what he did.

◉ He liked to eat apples.

○ An apple was named after him.

○ People could not remember the name Chapman.

11 In the story you get the idea that Johnny Appleseed

◉ was not a real person

○ was a very special person

○ was not very smart

○ was an unhappy person

12 Johnny was well-liked because of all his <u>good deeds</u>.

What does the phrase <u>good deeds</u> mean?

◉ friendliness

○ apple seeds

○ acts to help others

○ worthwhile lessons

13 The apples show some things we know about Johnny Appleseed.

Find the phrase that goes in the empty apple.

◉ was born in Massachusetts

○ wrote many stories, poems, plays

○ had a pet wolf

○ slept in a treetop

Directions: Read this story carefully. Then read each question. Darken the circle for the correct answer.

How to Get a Dog

by Delia Ephron

Tell your parents that you want a dog more than anything in this world. Promise that you'll take care of it. Cross your heart and hope to die. They won't have to do a thing. You'll walk it and feed it. Please. Please. Pretty-please. Pretty-please with sugar on top. Pretty-please with whipped cream and a cherry. Please, Mom, please. You are, too, old enough. When they say that you have to wait one more year, stamp your foot. Scream, "You never trust me; you never believe me. Why don't you trust me?"

Run to your room, slam the door, open the door, and yell, "It's not fair." Slam the door again. When your mother comes to your room, have the following conversation.

"That's enough," says she.

Say, "All right," as though it isn't.

"I said, 'That's enough.'"

"All I said was 'All right.'"

"It's not what you said, it's how you said it."

"Okay, Mom, but . . ." and repeat entire scene from "I want a dog more than anything in the world" to "Why don't you trust me?" Convince her.

conversation = talk

14 Who are these directions written for?

- ⬤ anyone
- ◯ a mother who does not want a dog
- ◯ a parent who wants a dog
- ◯ a child who wants a dog

15 What does the writer say you should promise your parents?

- ◯ You should not promise anything.
- ⬤ to walk and feed the dog
- ◯ to wait one more year
- ◯ to complain every day until you get the dog

16 The writer wants you to say "All right" so that it really means

- ◯ I'll stop
- ⬤ it's not all right
- ◯ who cares anyway
- ◯ you win

17 The author wrote

Convince her.

What is another way to say this?

- ◯ Tell her again.
- ◯ Make her believe you.
- ◯ Agree with her.
- ⬤ Disagree with her.

Language Arts

Directions: Read each sample. Darken the circle for the correct answer.

 Pretend that you are writing this sentence. Choose the words that belong in the blanks. Think of the rules you have learned.

Sample A

My dog _____.

- ○ running and barking
- ○ long brown hair
- ◉ is my best friend

 The correct answer is <u>is my best friend</u>. A complete sentence needs a subject and a verb. In this sentence, the subject is "My dog." The verb must agree with the subject. The verb "is" agrees with "My dog."

 Choose the answer carefully. Try each one in the sentence. Only one is correct. Pick the answer that belongs.

Sample B

This story is _____ than that one.

- ○ interesting
- ◉ more interesting
- ○ most interesting

 The correct answer is <u>more interesting</u>. This is the only answer that fits in the sentence.

Directions: Choose the word or words that belong in the blanks.

1   In the morning, I _____ down what I dreamed the night before.

   ○ writing

   ◉ write

   ○ writes

September 8, 2005

__(2)__

I read a good story about sisters. I should be nicer to my little sister.
Are you nice to your little sister?

__(3)__

Simon

---

2   ○ dear maria,

    ○ Dear maria,

    ◉ Dear Maria,

3   ◉ Your Cousin,

    ○ Your cousin,

    ○ your cousin,

4   I can be anything if I _____.

    ○ work at it

    ○ always have

    ○ flying with the birds

    ◉ not act lazy

5   **Choose the subject of the sentence. Darken the circle for the correct answer.**

   <u>Brenda and her mom</u> will go camping <u>this fall</u> with <u>her cousin Donna</u>.

   ◉   ○   ○

STOP

Lesson 3: Writing Strategies

Directions: Read each sample. Darken the circle for the correct answer.

Choose the sentence that best completes the story. Try each answer in place of the missing sentence. Only one belongs in the story. Pick the one that makes the most sense in the story.

Sample A

I have a chair in my room. I am not happy when I sit in it. _____.

- ○ I can see the park across the street.
- ● It is where I do my homework.
- ○ My desk is next to the chair.
- ○ It feels nice and soft.

 The correct answer is <u>It is where I do my homework</u>. This is the only sentence that can go at the end of this story. The other answers do not explain why the author does not like to sit in his chair.

Choose the best topic sentence for this story. Pick the answer that tells the main idea of the story. Try that answer in place of the missing sentence.

Sample B

_____. She sorts the clothes before they are washed. She cleans out the bird's cage.

- ● Cindy helps her father with the housework.
- ○ Cindy likes to wash the clothes.
- ○ Cindy lives in a big house.
- ○ Cindy is eight years old.

 The correct answer is <u>Cindy helps her father with the housework</u>. This is the only sentence that tells the main idea of the story. The other answers tell about Cindy. But they do not tell about the story.

Directions: Choose the sentence that best completes the story.

1   Mr. Han asked Ned to do some jobs. _____. Mr. Han always gives him a dollar for each job.

    ○ Ned asked Mr. Han if he could work for him.

    ○ Ned is lazy and does not like to work.

    ○ Ned told him that he could not help.

    ● Ned is a hard worker.

2   On rainy days, I sit in my chair and read. _____.

    ○ I play all day. My friends and I play fun games.

    ● I like to read fairy tales the best. I dream I'm a queen.

    ○ I watch TV every day. My mother does not like that.

    ○ I am a very good soccer player. I am on a team.

Directions: Choose the best topic sentence for the story.

3   _____. The farm is five miles from his school. He rides a bus to school because he lives too far to walk.

    ● Michael lives on a farm.

    ○ Michael is in third grade.

    ○ Michael likes to walk to school.

    ○ Michael's father is a farmer.

4   _____. The number of rings tells a tree's age. The more rings you count, the older the tree is.

    ○ Each ring stands for a year of growth.

    ○ Tree rings are narrow near the center.

    ● After a tree is cut down, you can see rings on the stump.

    ○ You might see many rings.

STOP

Directions: Read each sample. Darken the circle for the correct answer.

 Choose the sentence that is written correctly. Think of the rules you have learned. Pick the sentence that follows all the rules.

Sample A

○ Her and me went to the movies.

◉ My sister and I play together.

○ Us are good friends.

○ Them kids like to watch television.

 The correct answer is <u>My sister and I play together</u>. This is the only sentence with the correct pronouns.

 Choose the sentence that has the correct capitalization and punctuation. Pick the sentence that follows all the rules.

Sample B

○ The bird began to sing

○ the sound it made was beautiful.

○ I was very quiet?

◉ I didn't want the bird to stop.

 The correct answer is <u>I didn't want the bird to stop</u>. The sentence begins with a capital letter and ends with a period, which is correct.

Directions: Choose the word that can take the place of the underlined word.

1 <u>Whales</u> can be found in all oceans of the world.

    ○ He
    ○ She
    ○ It
    ● They

Directions: Choose the sentence that is written correctly.

2 ○ Hanging from the apple tree.
    ○ Flying through the night.
    ○ Hunting for the fox.
    ● Flying through the air is fun.

3 ○ The rain were falling.
    ● The rain rolled down the roof.
    ○ The rain made many trees to falled to Earth.
    ○ We hasn't seen so much rain in a long time.

Directions: Choose the sentence that has the correct capitalization and punctuation.

4 ● She likes to sit in her old chair.
    ○ She looks out the window!
    ○ she watches the clouds float by.
    ○ That is where she dreams

5 ○ Bear dens are not usually found in new Orleans, Louisiana.
    ○ You might see a bear in the mountains of idaho.
    ○ Polar bears live in Barrow Alaska.
    ● You would not see a bear on the streets of New York City.

STOP

Directions: Choose the word that belongs in the blank. Darken the circle for the correct answer.

Sample A

After Natasha _____ the song, everyone clapped.

- ◉ sing
- ○ singing
- ○ sang

Directions: Here is a story about an important food. Read this story. Then read each question. Darken the circle for the correct answer.

Bread

When you think of bread, what comes to mind? Do you think of a piece of white bread? If you lived in another country, you might have a very different idea of bread. A boy or girl in Mexico would think of tortillas. These are flat, round breads made from corn. People in India would think of chappatis. These are heavy pieces of round bread that are fried.

Bread is one of the most important foods. It is eaten more than any other food. It is also eaten in more places around the world than any other food.

The first bread was made about 12,000 years ago. People in the Middle East used seeds to make flour. They mixed the flour with water. Then they baked it on hot rocks.

Later, people in Egypt added something called yeast. Yeast made the bread rise. The Egyptians also built ovens. For hundreds of years, bread has been made in the same way.

Directions: Choose the words that belong in the blanks.

1 _____ bakes bread.

- ● A baker
- ○ The first bread
- ◐ In the oven

I love to eat bread. I __(2)__ Italian bread the best. I put a
lot of butter on a slice __(3)__ I eat it!

2 ◐ eat
   ○ bake
   ● like

3 ○ after
   ● before
   ○ to

Directions: Here is a story a student wrote about his father. The student made some mistakes. Read this story carefully. Then read each question. Darken the circle for the correct answer.

¹· My dad was a young boy when he came to America. ²· He life was never very easy. ³· He started to worked before he was eight years old. ⁴· My dad always worked hard. ⁵· That is why he became a success. ⁶· One day he opening a clothing store. ⁷· Soon he have many stores. ⁸· He made the American dream come true.

4 **Choose the best way to write sentence 2.**

- ● His life was never very easy.
- ○ Him life was never very easy.
- ○ Its life was never very easy.
- ○ It is best as it is.

5 **Choose the best way to write sentence 3.**

- ○ He started to working before he was eight years old.
- ● He started to works before he was eight years old.
- ○ He started to work before he was eight years old.
- ○ It is best as it is.

6 **Choose the best way to write sentence 6.**

- ○ Opening a clothing store one day.
- ● One day he opened a clothing store.
- ○ He opening a clothing store one day.
- ○ It is best as it is.

7 **Choose the best way to write sentence 7.**

- ● Soon he had many stores.
- ○ Soon he having many stores.
- ○ Soon he haded many stores.
- ○ It is best as it is.

Directions: Here is a story about Kristi Yamaguchi, a figure-skating star. Read this story carefully. Then read each question. Darken the circle for the correct answer.

Skating for Gold

The year 1992 was a good one for Kristi Yamaguchi. That year she won gold medals in the United States and World figure-skating contests. In the 1992 Winter Olympics, she won gold for the United States. Three medals in one year!

Kristi is awesome! She twists and turns. She flies through the air. It's hard to believe that Kristi was born with a turned-in foot. She had to wear special shoes. They helped her foot stay straight. When she was four years old, her parents sent her to dance lessons. They thought dancing would help her walk better. They thought it would make her legs strong. When she was six, she started skating lessons. Even at six, Kristi skated great.

United States skater Dorothy Hamill won a gold medal in the 1976 Olympics. That was one year before Kristi started skating. Dorothy was Kristi's hero. Kristi says, "Every little girl wanted to be just like Dorothy." Kristi wanted to be like Dorothy, too.

All Kristi's hard work paid off in 1992. She became a gold medal winner just like her hero. Kristi Yamaguchi has lived her dream.

8 **A student found out more about Kristi Yamaguchi. Choose the best topic sentence for her story.**

_____. When she was training, Kristi had to get up at 4 A.M. She practiced skating before school. She also went to a dance class once a week.

- ● Kristi worked hard to be a winner.
- ○ Kristi admired Dorothy Hamill.
- ○ Kristi always wanted to ice skate.
- ○ Kristi grew up in California.

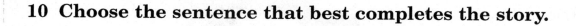

9 **Choose the sentence that is written correctly.**

- ○ To win the contest.
- ○ Dancing to music.
- ● The ice is very slippery.
- ○ Ice skating always fun.

10 **Choose the sentence that best completes the story.**

Figure skating is done on a large, egg-shaped rink. _____. Each skater takes a turn skating around the ice.

- ○ They all do jumps and turns.
- ● Music is played.
- ○ The fans clapped after every jump.
- ○ It takes years of practice to be in the Olympics.

11 Choose the word that is the subject of the sentence.

The <u>skater</u> is the most <u>important</u> <u>person</u> on the <u>ice</u>.

●   ◯   ◯   ◯

Directions: Choose the words that belong in the blanks.

> November 22, 2005
>
> (12) _____
>
> It was fun reading about Kristi Yamaguchi. Now I want to learn how to skate. Would you like to borrow my book?
>
> (13) _____
> Lucia

12 ◯ dear carol,
    ● Dear Carol,
    ◯ Dear carol
    ◯ Dear Carol

13 ◯ Your Friend
    ◯ your friend,
    ● Your friend,
    ◯ Your friend

STOP

Sample A

Brooke ate breakfast. She went out the door. She waited for the school bus. When the bus came, Brooke climbed aboard.

Find the picture that shows where Brooke was going.

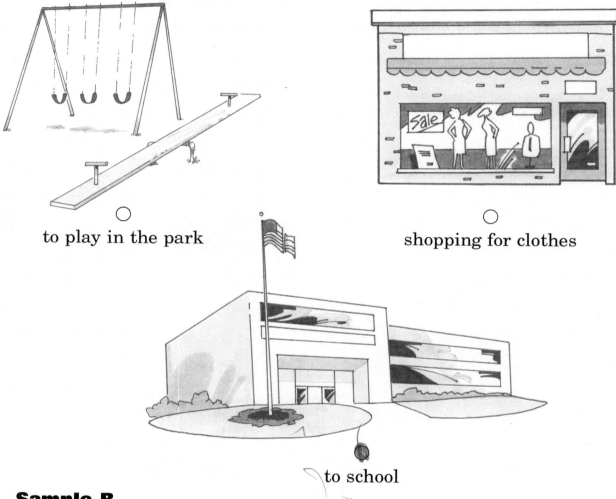

○ to play in the park

○ shopping for clothes

to school

Sample B

Choose the words that belong in the blank.

My house _____.

- ○ and my father
- ○ painting yellow
- ● is old
- ○ very comfortable

STOP

Part 1

Make-Believe

It's fun to make-believe. You can be anything you want to be. It's fun to read stories that are make-believe, too.

First, you will read a poem about a boy who pretends. Then, you will read some stories about things that are not real.

Directions: Here is a poem about a boy who makes-believe while he is sick. Read this poem carefully. Then read each question. Darken the circle for the correct answer.

The Land of Counterpane

by Robert Louis Stevenson

counterpane = bedspread or quilt

When I was sick and lay in bed,
    I had two pillows at my head,
And all my toys beside me lay,
    To keep me happy all the day.

And sometimes for an hour or so,
    I watched my toy soldiers go,
With different uniforms and drills.
    Among the bed-clothes, through the hills.

And sometimes sent my ships in fleets,
    All up and down among the sheets;
Or brought my trees and houses out,
    And planted cities all about.

I was the giant great and still,
    That sits upon the pillow hill,
And sees before him valley and plain,
    The pleasant land of counterpane.

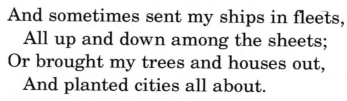

1 **Where is the boy in this poem?**

- ○ in a place called Counterpane
- ◉ in his bed
- ○ in the countryside

2 **Which of these ideas from the poem are real?**

- ○ The boy is a giant.
- ○ The boy plants trees.
- ◉ The boy has a set of toy ships.

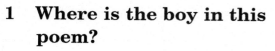

3 Find the picture that shows how the boy feels.

○   ○   ○

4 How does the boy think of his toys?

- ● The toys are real things.
- ○ The toys don't work very well.
- ○ The toys are old.

5 I watched my toy soldiers <u>go</u>.

A word that means the opposite of <u>go</u> is

- ○ stay
- ● leave
- ○ move

6 Choose the words that belong in the blank.

Our soldiers _____.

- ○ going home
- ● climb the hills
- ○ on the bed

7 Find the word that can take the place of <u>the boy</u> in the sentence below.

<u>The boy</u> played with his toys in bed.

- ● He
- ○ She
- ○ It

Directions: Here is a story about a parrot. Read this story carefully. Then read each question. Darken the circle for the correct answer.

THE GREEN CHICKEN

perch = a resting place

by Alvin Schwartz

parrot = a bird

Jill's friend left his parrot, Edward, with her for a few days. Jill put Edward's perch in a sunny window in the kitchen. It was a pleasant place for him to rest. She fastened a long, thin chain to one of his legs so that he could fly when he wanted to, but could not fly away.

Edward had learned to speak a few words his owners had taught him. "Good morning!" he would croak. "Have you had your breakfast yet? Have a bit of buttered toast. It's awfully good."

peering = looking

But at Jill's house, Edward had nothing to say. He sat quietly on his perch looking this way and that, his big golden eyes peering sadly out of his bright-green feathers.

"What is that hairy thing in the corner?" he asked himself. It was Jill's cat, Beatrice, staring at him.

"Whatever can that be?" Beatrice thought. "Oh, of course. It is a green chicken. How delicious it looks!"

Edward stared back at Beatrice. "That is an enemy," he told himself. He ruffled his feathers, rattled his chain, tapped his bill nervously on his perch, and waited.

Beatrice crept out of the corner, her body pressed to the floor, her tiny yellow eyes fixed on Edward. Edward watched anxiously, raising first one foot, then the other.

anxiously = with fear

Suddenly Beatrice sprang into the air and landed next to him.

"Good morning," Edward cried out in fright. "Have you had your breakfast yet?" Beatrice was so startled she fell off the perch and landed on her head.

"Have a piece of buttered toast," Edward croaked. "It's awfully good."

"It's not a green chicken," Beatrice thought. "It's a green person!" She ran from the room and didn't go near Edward again.

8 Jill's friend left Edward with Jill because

○ Edward was lonely

○ Edward needed a baby sitter

◉ Edward needed speaking lessons

9 Why did Edward have a chain around his leg?

○ to keep him from falling off the perch

○ to keep him quiet

◉ to keep him from flying away

10 What did Beatrice think Edward was?

○ a parrot

◉ a chicken

○ a cat

11 At the end, why did Beatrice think Edward was a person?

○ Edward ate buttered toast.

○ Edward knocked her off the perch.

◉ Edward spoke to her.

12 Suddenly Beatrice <u>sprang</u> into the air.

Another word for <u>sprang</u> is

◉ jumped

○ sang

○ ran

13 The window was a <u>pleasant</u> place to rest.

A word that means the ⬚opposite⬚ of <u>pleasant</u> is

○ warm

● awful

○ pleasing

14 Find the sentence that best completes the story.

Beatrice watched Edward. _____. She tried to catch him.

● She practiced speaking to him.

○ She ate chicken every day.

○ She wanted to have him for lunch.

15 Choose the word that belongs in the blank.

I don't like the way he keeps _____ at me.

○ stare

● staring

○ stared

Directions: Here is a story about a sock. Read this story carefully. Then read each question. Darken the circle for the correct answer.

Irwin the Sock

by David J. Klein

My name is Irwin. I am a sock. I have had a long and exciting life.

I remember when Irma, my mate, and I were made. After we were made, we were squeezed into a box. The next light we saw was in a clothing store. Within an hour, Irma and I were bought by Mrs. Davidson.

Mrs. Davidson had gotten us for her son, Phil. Phil was a nice boy of ten. In the winter Phil stayed inside a lot. He practiced his violin. His feet were clean and his nails were neatly trimmed.

When spring arrived, soccer season began. Phil's feet got smelly. He pounded us as he ran and kicked. We did not like being worn for sports.

We got older. Phil wore us less and less. The last time I saw Irma was the day of a music contest. Phil was very nervous. He grabbed a thread on his other leg and began to pull and pull. Phil looked down to see what it came from. He realized that the thread on the floor was once his left sock. Irma never had a chance.

violin = something that makes music

Phil won the contest. He told his mother that we were his lucky socks. She could not throw me out.

Phil never wore me again. But if he has a soccer game or has to play his violin, he puts me in his pocket. I miss my dear Irma. But it's still exciting to be with Phil when his team wins a game or when he is on stage.

In a way, Irma's passing gave me a second chance, a new life.

16 What was the first thing that happened to Irwin and Irma after they were made?

- ○ They were worn by Phil when he played soccer.
- ○ They were worn by Phil when he played the violin.
- ○ They were sold.
- ◉ They were put into a box.

17 Why didn't Irwin and Irma like soccer season?

- ◉ They got smelly.
- ○ They did not like to lose.
- ○ They had to go outside.
- ○ They got older.

18 Why did Phil pull Irma apart?

- ◉ He thought she was lucky.
- ○ He was excited.
- ○ He was nervous.
- ○ He didn't like her.

19 Why does Phil put Irwin in his pocket?

- ○ He can't wear Irwin on his feet.
- ○ He thinks Irwin brings good luck.
- ○ He is afraid to rip Irwin.
- ● He doesn't want his mother to throw Irwin out.

20 Which idea could not happen in real life?

- ● In the winter Phil only stayed inside.
- ○ Irwin did not like being worn for sports.
- ◐ Phil got nervous during music contests.
- ○ Irma fell apart.

21 How does Irwin feel at the end of the story?

thankful because he's still useful

happy because Phil doesn't wear him on his feet

sad because Phil has forgotten him

excited because he gets to play soccer

22 If you wanted to name a pair of your socks like Irwin and Irma were named, what could you call them?

- ○ Andres and Anna
- ○ Bill and Silvia
- ◉ Aaron and Erin
- ○ Daniel and Michelle

23 Two matching socks are called a <u>pair</u>.

What is something else that comes in a pair?

- ○ hats
- ◉ jackets
- ○ gloves
- ○ skirts

24 Choose the word that belongs in the blank.

Do you _____ socks every day?

- ○ wore
- ◉ wear
- ○ wears
- ○ wearing

25 Choose the word that belongs in the blank for <u>both</u> sentences.

Turn off the _____ when you leave the room.

A box full of feathers is very _____.

- ○ radio
- ◉ large
- ○ water
- ◉ light

Directions: Here is a fairy tale. Read this story carefully. Then read each question. Darken the circle for the correct answer.

The Dragon of Worchester

by Jesse Lawrence

King John of Worchester was the richest king in all the land. Townsfolk often came to the castle asking for money. King John always refused.

The people began to get angry. More and more people started to come to the castle. As they did, King John began to worry. One morning more than fifty people came. "Remove them," King John told the guards. The people did not want to go. They gave the guards a hard time. Two people were put in the dungeon.

dungeon = underground jail

King John was worried. He knew more people would come the next day. That evening he set out to find help. He walked to a cave. "Dragon of Worchester," the king yelled inside. "I come to you in need."

King John heard a voice. "What is it, oh richest king?"

"I am worried about my people. I need someone to move them away. I can pay you a lot of money."

There was a long silence. Finally, the dragon spoke. "I will be there tomorrow as you have asked."

The next morning the king woke early to look for the dragon. He was nowhere to be found. By noon over one hundred people were gathered in front of the castle. They were all very angry.

"Coins for the people!" they yelled.

Then loud footsteps shook the ground. It was the dragon. King John ran to a window to speak to him. "I'm so glad to see you," he told the dragon. "Do whatever is needed to rid me of these townsfolk."

The dragon started to whack the castle with his tail. The side wall broke. Gold and silver came pouring out. The people heard the noise and rushed to see what it was. A large cheer went up as they grabbed the coins. After all the coins were gone, the people left.

townsfolk = people who live in a town

"What have you done?" King John screamed to the dragon.

"I have helped you just as you asked. The people are gone." And with that, he disappeared.

26 Why did the townsfolk show up at the castle?

- ● They were afraid of the dragon.
- ○ They were having a party.
- ○ They wanted to see King John.
- ○ They hoped to get money.

27 How would you describe King John?

- ○ selfish and cruel
- ○ rich and kind
- ○ happy and fair
- ● brave and giving

28 Why did King John begin to worry?

- ● He was afraid the townsfolk would hurt him.
- ○ He thought the townsfolk might hurt themselves.
- ○ He was in need of more money.
- ○ He felt his guards needed help.

29 How did the dragon get rid of the townsfolk?

- ○ He scared them away.
- ○ He took them to his secret cave.
- ◉ He gave them what they wanted.
- ○ He tricked them.

30 How do you know that the dragon didn't like King John?

- ○ The dragon told King John he would not help him.
- ○ The dragon helped the townsfolk.
- ○ The dragon did not show up on time.
- ◉ The dragon disappeared at the end.

31 This story teaches a lesson. What lesson does King John learn?

- ○ You should save your money.
- ◉ You should be kind to others.
- ○ You should not trust dragons.
- ○ You should hide from danger.

32 Choose the sentence that is written correctly.

- ◉ Them wanted money from King John.
- ○ The dragon helped his.
- ○ Those townsfolk were angry.
- ○ Her asked for some money.

33 Choose the word that belongs in the blank.

The dragon was _____ than King John.

- ● nice
- ○ nicer
- ○ nicest
- ○ nicely

34 Choose the words that belong in the blank.

The king _____.

- ○ married to a queen
- ○ and his guards
- ○ worrying about the townsfolk
- ● rules the country

35 Karla wrote this story about being a king. Choose the best topic sentence for the story.

_____. You must rule the people in your country. But you need to make them happy. You want them to like you.

- ○ Kings are rich people.
- ○ It must be fun to be king.
- ○ I don't know any kings.
- ○ It is hard to be a good king.

Directions: Here is a nursery rhyme. It is very old. Read this rhyme. Then read each question. Darken the circle for the correct answer.

OLD MOTHER HUBBARD

by Mother Goose

Old Mother Hubbard
   Went to the cupboard,
To give her poor dog a bone;
   But when she got there
The cupboard was bare,
   And so the poor dog had none.

She went to the baker's
   To buy him some bread;
When she came back
   The dog was dead.

She went to the undertaker's
   To buy him a coffin;
When she got back
   The dog was laughin'.

Directions: There are more verses to this nursery rhyme. Some of them are below. Choose the word or words that belong in the blanks.

She went to the __(36)__
  To buy him a hat;
When she came back
  He was feeding the cat.

She went to the barber's
  To buy him a __(37)__ ;
When she came back
  He was dancing a jig.

She went to the fruiterer's
  To buy him some fruit;
When she came __(38)__
  He was playing the flute.

She went to the cobbler's
  To buy him some shoes;
When she came back
  He was reading the __(39)__ .

36 ○ hatter's
   ● pet store
   ○ undertaker's
   ○ cupboard

37 ○ shave
   ○ haircut
   ○ wig
   ● hat

38 ● home
   ○ mute
   ○ back
   ○ to her

39 ● paper
   ○ lose
   ○ sack
   ○ news

STOP

Being the Best You Can Be

If you want to do well, first you have to try. Sometimes it is hard to do well. But you should always try to be the best you can be.

Now you will read about some people who have done great things. These people did not let anything stop them.

Directions: Here is a story about a baseball star. His name is Larry Doby. He was one of the first African-Americans to play in the major leagues. Read this story. Then read each question. Darken the circle for the correct answer.

One of Baseball's Best

At one time black and white baseball players could not play together. The major leagues were for white people. Black players had to play in the Negro league. That's the way it was until 1947. In that year Jackie Robinson and Larry Doby were the first African-Americans to play in the major leagues.

Larry was a home run hitter. He became one of the best players in the Negro league. In 1947 he hit more home runs than any other player. That was the year the owner of the Cleveland Indians asked Larry to play for them. Larry Doby joined the major leagues. Larry helped the Cleveland Indians win many games.

Fifty years later, in 1997, there were parties to celebrate what Larry Doby did. At one of the parties in Cleveland, 43,000 people stood up and cheered him. In 1998 Larry was picked for the Baseball Hall of Fame. Larry once said, "I wanted to play the best I could." Larry Doby was a great baseball player. He is also a great American.

league = a group of teams

40 Why did the Cleveland Indians want Larry Doby to play for them?

- ○ because he was a great American
- ○ because he played all kinds of sports
- ◉ because he was a home run hitter
- ○ because he was in the Negro league

41 How is Larry Doby like Jackie Robinson?

- ○ They loved to play basketball.
- ○ They were born in 1947.
- ○ They both helped the Cleveland Indians win many games.
- ◉ They were the first African-Americans to play major league baseball.

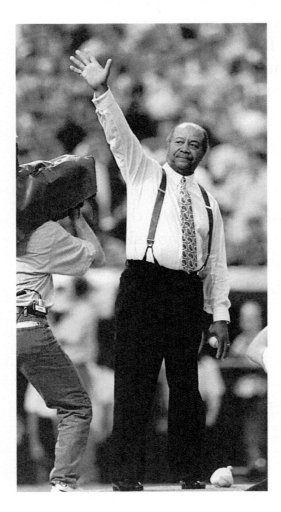

42 Why was Larry being honored in 1997?

- ○ He was one of the first black men to play major league baseball.
- ◉ He had been elected into the Baseball Hall of Fame.
- ○ He was celebrating his birthday.
- ○ He had just helped the Cleveland Indians win a game.

43 Look at the photo of Larry Doby at the party in Cleveland. How do you think he felt?

- ◉ happy because people remembered what he did
- ○ sad because many people had not heard of him
- ○ glad because he was playing baseball
- ○ angry because he could not play baseball

44 In 1997 there were parties to <u>celebrate</u> what Larry Doby did. Another word for <u>celebrate</u> is

- ○ tell
- ○ honor
- ○ refuse
- ● show

45 A student wrote a story about Larry Doby. Choose the sentence that best completes the story.

> Larry Doby was always a good ballplayer. As a child, he was the best player on his team. _____.

- ○ He played stickball in Camden, South Carolina. In high school he played all kinds of sports.
- ○ In 1948 the Cleveland Indians won the World Series. That was the last time they won.
- ● He grew up to become a home run champ. He helped the Cleveland Indians win the World Series in 1948.
- ○ He played for the Kansas City Monarchs in the Negro league. He was paid $350.

46 Choose the sentence that is written correctly.

- ○ To hit the ball.
- ○ Playing the game of baseball.
- ● He have not heard of Larry Doby.
- ○ You play stickball with a stick.

47 Choose the sentence that best completes the story.

The World Series is played at the end of every baseball season.
_____. The first team to win four games wins the series.

- ◉ Opening day of the baseball season is in the spring.
- ○ The Cleveland Indians won the World Series in 1948.
- ○ The two top teams play each other.
- ○ People have been playing baseball since the 1800s.

48 Choose the subject of the sentence.

The <u>party</u> was a <u>surprise</u> for the <u>special</u> <u>guest</u>.
    ◉   ○   ○   ○

49 Choose the word that belongs in the blank.

The Cleveland Indians were the _____ team in baseball in 1948.

- ◉ good
- ○ better
- ○ best
- ○ bestest

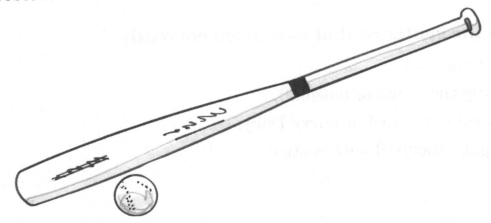

Directions: Choose the words with the correct capital letters and punctuation for the blanks.

June 16, 2005

(50)

I read about Larry Doby. He was an interesting man. I would like to send the book to you. I think you'll like it.

(51)

Ali

50 ○ dear jane
  ○ Dear jane
  ● Dear Jane,

51 ● Your cousin
  ○ Your cousin,
  ○ your cousin

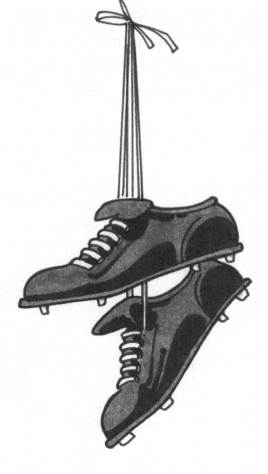

Directions: Here is a student's report about Margaret Knight. The student made some mistakes. Read this story carefully. Then read each question. Darken the circle for the correct answer.

Margaret Knight — Young Inventor

[1.] Margaret Knight is my hero. [2.] She works in a cotton mill in the 1850s. [3.] A cotton mill were a place where they made cloth. [4.] Margaret's nickname was Matty. [5.] One day Matty saw someone get hurt. [6.] A girl was stuck by the sharp point of a machine. [7.] After that Matty inventing a new machine that was safer. [8.] Her was only 12 years old when she invented the machine. [9.] Matty invented about ninety more things during her life.

52 Choose the best way to write sentence 2.

○ She is working in a cotton mill in the 1850s.

○ She has worked in a cotton mill in the 1850s.

○ She worked in a cotton mill in the 1850s.

○ Best as it is.

53 Choose the best way to write sentence 3.

○ Cotton mills were a place where they made cloth.

○ A cotton mill was a place where they made cloth.

○ Cotton mills was a place where they made cloth.

○ Best as it is.

54 Choose the best way to write sentence 7.

○ After that Matty invented a new machine that was safer.

○ Matty inventing a new machine that was safer after that.

○ After that Matty has invented a new machine that was safer.

○ Best as it is.

55 Choose the best way to write sentence 8.

○ Her was only 12 years old when her invented the machine.

○ She was only 12 years old when she invented the machine.

○ She was only 12 years old when her invented the machine.

○ Best as it is.

Directions: Here is a story about a writer. Her name is Amy Tan. Read this story. Then read each question. Darken the circle for the correct answer.

Meet Amy Tan

When Amy Tan was a little girl, her family moved a lot. Amy missed her old friends. She wrote letters to these old friends. Amy did not want her letters to be boring. So she made up things to write about. That's how Amy learned to tell colorful tales. No wonder she grew up to be a book author.

Amy is an Asian-American. Her mother and father came from China. Amy was born and raised in California.

When she was young, Amy didn't like her nose. Amy did not want to look Chinese. Sometimes she wore a clothespin on her nose. Now Amy is proud to look Chinese. Her stories are about Chinese people who live in America.

Today her writing is famous. Her best known book is *The Joy Luck Club*. It is about four Chinese women who came to the United States. The book tells of how they raised their children in America.

56 Amy wrote made-up stories in her letters because

- ● she was lonely
- ○ she did not want to bore her friends
- ○ she wanted to be an author when she grew up
- ○ she did not like her looks

57 Today Amy Tan's writing is <u>famous</u>.

Another word for <u>famous</u> is

- ○ forgotten
- ○ colorful
- ○ beautiful
- ● well-known

58 Why did Amy probably write to her friends?

- ● She wanted to stay friends with them.
- ○ She did not want to see them.
- ○ She had to practice her writing.
- ○ She was asked to write to them by her parents.

59 Amy writes about growing up in America because

- ● that is what she wrote in her letters
- ○ she does not know about China
- ○ that is the life she knows
- ○ she writes fairy tales

60 The story says Amy was "raised in California."

What does that mean?

- ● She left California after she was born.
- ○ She liked living in California.
- ○ She grew up in California.
- ○ She moved to California.

Choose the words that belong in the blanks.

I wish I were a writer like Amy Tan. I __(61)__ writing all the time.
__(62)__ writing, I think of something funny that has happened to me.

61 ● repeat
○ learn
○ read
○ practice

62 ○ Because
● After
○ While
○ Under

63 Choose the sentence that best completes the story.

When I was a little girl, I liked to read. _____. Now that I am older,
I can buy my own books.

○ I go to the bookstore all the time.
● My mother bought me all the books I loved.
○ I don't care to read anymore.
○ When I was a baby, my mother read to me.

64 **A student found out a lot about Amy Tan. She wrote a story about her. Choose the best topic sentence for her story.**

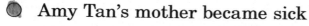 _____. She read a book a day when she was a kid. She loved fairy tales and the Laura Ingalls Wilder books.

- ⬤ Amy always loved to read.
- ◯ Amy did very well in school.
- ◯ Amy had a job writing speeches.
- ◯ Amy remembers all of her teachers.

65 **Choose the sentence that has the correct capitalization and punctuation.**

- ◯ Amy is asian-american.
- ⬤ Her Mother and Father came from China.
- ◯ Amy was born in California
- ◯ Today she lives in San Francisco.

66 **Choose the sentence that has the correct capitalization and punctuation.**

- ⬤ Amy Tan's mother became sick
- ◯ Amy made a promise to her?
- ◯ her mother got better.
- ◯ They visited China together.

CHINA

67 **Choose the sentence that is written correctly.**

- ● He have written many stories.
- ○ You can write on a computer.
- ○ Science fiction stories is the best.
- ○ I likes to write plays.

68 **Choose the sentence that is written correctly.**

- ○ Writing at night.
- ● She loves reading.
- ○ Dreams to be told.
- ○ To be an author.

69 **Choose the words that belong in the blank.**

_____ wrote down her dreams.

- ● The poet
- ○ Tomorrow afternoon
- ○ When the sun
- ○ Exciting and sad

70 **Choose the sentence that best completes the story.**

When I'm alone, I pretend I am a writer. _____.

- ○ I meet my friends. We all play together.
- ○ I go to the kitchen. There is always something to eat.
- ○ The dog comes into the house. He has muddy feet.
- ● I sit at my desk and think. Then I write little stories.

Section
B

Mathematics

About Section B: Mathematics
This section of the book has been developed to refresh basic skills, familiarize your child with test formats and directions, and teach test-taking strategies. This section of the book is divided into three components: Lessons, Review Tests, and Comprehensive Test.

Note: In order to answer some of the problems in this section, students will need a ruler with measurements marked off in both inches and centimeters.

Lessons
There is one lesson for each of the nine math skills assessed on the CTB-TerraNova Mathematics test. Each lesson contains:

- *Try This:* a skill strategy that enables your child to approach each lesson in a logical manner
- *Sample:* to familiarize your child with test-taking items
- *Think It Through:* the correct answer to the sample item and an explanation that tells why the correct answer is correct and why the incorrect answers are wrong
- two practice questions based on the lesson and modeled on the kinds of items found on the CTB-TerraNova

Review Test
The lessons are followed by a short Review Test that covers all the skills in the lessons. This section is designed to provide your child with independent practice that will familiarize him or her with the testing situation.

Comprehensive Test
The last component in this section is a Comprehensive Test. This test gives your child an opportunity to take a test under conditions that parallel those he or she will face when taking the CTB-TerraNova Mathematics test.

In order to simulate the CTB-TerraNova test as closely as possible, we have suggested time limits for the Comprehensive Test. This will enable your child to experience test taking under the same structured conditions that apply when achievement tests are administered. Furthermore, your child will have a final opportunity to apply the skills he or she has learned in this section prior to taking the CTB-TerraNova.

The recommended time limits are:
    Part 1: 15 minutes
    Part 2: 45 minutes

Answer Key
The Answer Key at the back of the book contains the answers for all the problems found in this section.

Mathematics

Directions: Read each question carefully. Darken the circle for the correct answer.

 When reading word names for numbers, imagine filling in the number from left to right.

Sample

Which of these is three hundred six?

- ○ 36
- ○ 360
- ● 306
- ○ 603

 The correct answer is 306. Since there are no tens, a zero goes in the tens place.

---

1 **What number is shown by the blocks in the picture below?**

- ○ 407
- ● 47
- ○ 74
- ○ 704

2 **Jan had the highest score on her bowling team last week. What was Jan's score?**

- ○ 128
- ◎ 140
- ○ 134
- ● 98

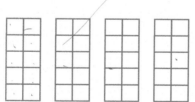

Last week's
Bowling Scores

105
128
140
116
98
134

········ Lesson 2: Computation and Numerical Estimation

Directions: Read each question carefully. Darken the circle for the correct answer.

Try This

Read word problems carefully. This helps you understand exactly what is being asked for.

Sample

In Ms. Royster's class, the students have 17 pet dogs and 14 pet cats. How many pet dogs and cats are there in all?

- ● 31
- ○ 21
- ◐ 41
- ○ 184
- ○ None of these

Think It Through The correct answer is <u>31</u>. To find the total number of pets, add the number of dogs and the number of cats. $17 + 14 = \underline{31}$.

---

1 9 + 6 =

- ○ 96
- ○ 63
- ○ 56
- ○ 54
- ● None of these

2 Tom bought three items at a baseball game. Which amount is closest to the amount Tom spent?

- ○ $40
- ○ $30
- ○ $20
- ● $10

  $6.00 $2.00 $9.00

72

Lesson 3: Operation Concepts

Directions: Read each question carefully. Darken the circle for the correct answer.

Read the directions for the problem carefully. Then try each of the answers in the problem.

Sample

Look at the number sentence below. Which number in the box makes it true?

$4 + \boxed{} = 12$

- ○ 4
- ○ 6
- ● 8
- ○ 10

The correct answer is 8, since $4 + 8 = 12$.

---

1   Ian and Sharon bought two pizzas. They carried them home. On the way, they ate three slices. How many slices were left when they got home?

- ○ 17
- ○ 15
- ● 13
- ○ 5

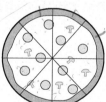 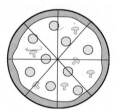

2   Bob bought an apple for 40 cents and a roll for 30 cents. Which number sentence shows what he spent in all?

- ○ 40 + 30 = 70
- ● 40 − 30 = 10
- ○ 30 + 10 = 40
- ○ 10 + 30 = 40

Lesson 4: Measurement

Directions: Read each question carefully. Darken the circle for the correct answer.

Try This

When counting time on a clock, try to picture the minute hand moving forward. This can help you keep track of minutes.

Sample

The clock shows the time it is now. How many minutes are there until the minute hand reaches the 10?

- ○ 50 minutes
- ◉ 25 minutes
- ○ 10 minutes
- ○ 5 minutes

Think It Through

The correct answer is <u>25 minutes</u>. The minute hand is now on the 5. As it moves forward, each number reached means that five minutes have passed. To get to 10, it goes past 5 numbers. 5 x 5 = 25 minutes.

---

1   **Use the centimeter side of your ruler to solve this problem.**

   What is the length of the longer side of the rectangle?

   - ○ 3 cm
   - ○ 4 cm
   - ◉ 5 cm
   - ○ 6 cm

2   **Which is most likely measured in inches?**

   - ◉ the amount of juice in a cup
   - ○ the weight of a piano
   - ○ the width of a photo
   - ○ the height of a tall building

Lesson 5: Geometry and Spatial Sense

Directions: Read each question carefully. Darken the circle for the correct answer.

 Try This When you are asked how a figure changes, draw it on paper. Fold it, turn it, or slide it.

Sample

Georgia flipped the figure over the line shown. What figure did she get?

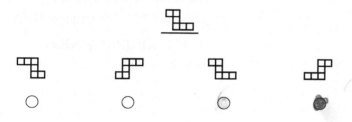

○   ○   ◉   ●

Think It Through  The correct answer is ⌐F. When a figure is flipped over a line below it, top becomes bottom and bottom becomes top.

---

1 **Which two figures are the same?**

- ○ R and U
- ○ T and V
- ○ V and S
- ◉ S and U

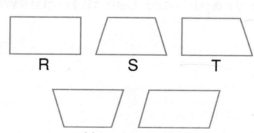

2 **Which figure has four sides that are the same length?**

- ○ circle
- ○ triangle
- ○ rectangle
- ◉ square

STOP

Lesson 6: Data Analysis, Statistics, and Probability

Directions: Read each question carefully. Darken the circle for the correct answer.

> **Try This** Always read problems carefully. Make sure you understand the question. Or else, you may give the wrong answer!

Sample

Todd spun the spinner shown. Which number does he have the best chance of landing on?

○ 1
○ 2
○ 3
◉ 4

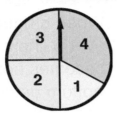

 **Think It Through** The correct answer is 4. The spinner has the best chance of landing on the number with the largest space. The number 4 is in the largest space.

Some students were asked how many telephones they had at home. Study the graph and use it to answer problems 1 and 2.

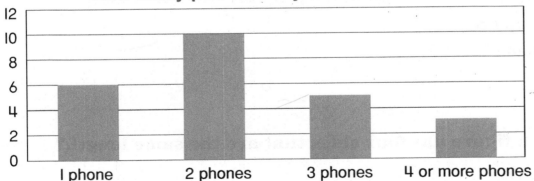

How many phones do you have at home?

1 How many students have 2 telephones at home?

◉ 10 students
○ 16 students
○ 15 students
○ 12 students

2 How many students were asked about telephones?

○ 10
○ 14
◉ 24
○ 25

Directions: Read each question carefully. Darken the circle for the correct answer.

 This question asks about a pattern. See how you can get from the first number to the next. See if you can use the same rule for the next numbers.

Sample

Look at the pattern below. What number comes next?

40, 60, 80, 100, ___

- ○ 101
- ○ 110
- ◉ 120
- ○ 180

 The correct answer is 120.
40 + 20 = 60. 60 + 20 = 80.
80 + 20 = 100. 100 + 20 = 120.

---

1 How many squares will there be in the next figure of the pattern?

- ○ 25
- ◉ 16
- ◉ 13
- ○ 10

  **?**
_____

2 Today's date is Wednesday, May 9. Felo's birthday is two weeks from this Friday. When is Felo's birthday?

- ○ May 11
- ◉ May 18
- ○ May 23
- ◉ May 25

S	M	T	W	T	F	S
		1	2	3	4	5
6	7	8	9	10	11	12
13	14	15	16	17	18	19
20	21	22	23	24	25	26
27	28	29	30	31		

May

STOP

Lesson 8: Problem Solving and Reasoning

Directions: Read each question carefully. Darken the circle for the correct answer.

Try This | Test each answer listed. This will help you get rid of incorrect answers.

Sample

Abe has an even number of quarters in his pocket. How much money could he have in quarters?

○ $0.75
○ $0.80
○ $0.90
◉ $1.00

Think It Through The correct answer is $1.00. Abe could have 4 quarters totaling $1.00. Choice A does not work. 3 quarters total $0.75 and 3 is an odd number. Choices B and C do not work. You cannot make those amounts with quarters.

1　**Every morning Peter adds 5 rocks to his rock garden. Every evening a squirrel hides one of the rocks. How many days will it take Peter to have 100 rocks in his rock garden?**

◎ 20 days
○ 24 days
◉ 25 days
○ 100 days

100

2　**Coco bought two large pieces of chalk. She received the change shown from a $1 bill.**

How much did each piece of chalk cost?

○ 19 cents
◉ 14 cents
○ 24 cents
◎ 31 cents

25
35
60

Lesson 9: Communication

Directions: Read each question carefully. Darken the circle for the correct answer.

 Try This Look at the picture carefully. Make sure you understand all the information in it.

Sample

Tasha is 11 years old. How much will it cost for Tasha and her mother to attend a movie?

- ○ $16
- ● $14
- ○ $8
- ○ $6

```
......................................
:        Movie Ticket Prices         :
:                                     :
:   Children (under age 12)    $6     :
:                                     :
:   Adults                     $8     :
......................................
```

 **Think It Through**

The correct answer is $14. Since Tasha is under age 12, she pays $6. Her mother pays $8. In all, they pay $6 + $8 = $14.

---

1 How far is it from Pocaville to Wimlette along Route 64?

- ● 92 miles
- ○ 82 miles
- ○ 47 miles
- ○ 45 miles

Route 64	
West	**East**
←	→
Pocaville	Wimlette
45 miles	47 miles

2 Pia starts at her house. She walks three blocks south. Then she walks two blocks west. Where is she now?

- ○ at the school
- ● at the park
- ○ at the pet shop
- ○ at the bus stop

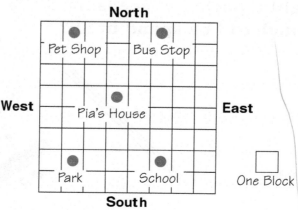

Directions: Read each question carefully. Darken the circle for the correct answer.

1 **38 + 7 =**

- ○ 35
- ● 45
- ○ 108
- ○ 315
- ○ None of these

2 **4 × 8 =**

- ○ 12
- ○ 24
- ○ 36
- ○ 48
- ● None of these

3 **68 – 5 =**

- ● 63
- ○ 73
- ○ 18
- ○ 62
- ○ None of these

4 **Thomas bought a packet of seeds for $0.79 and a pencil for $0.55. How much did he spend in all?**

- ● $1.34
- ○ $1.33
- ○ $1.24
- ○ $1.23
- ● None of these

5 Ursula had the pennies shown below. She gave three of the pennies to her friend, Wei. What number sentence tells how many pennies Ursula had left?

○ 7 + 3 = 10
○ 6 + 3 = 9
○ 6 − 3 = 3
● 7 − 3 = 4

6 Arnold has two dollars. Which item can he **not** buy?

○ box of crayons
○ ball
○ bag of potato chips
● box of cookies

$1.89 $1.29   89¢ $2.19

7 Which number is 306 + 387 closest to?

○ 600
● 700
○ 800
○ 900

8 What number is missing in the number pattern?

50, 100, 150, ___, 250

○ 300
● 200
○ 151
○ 160

9   What number is shown by the blocks in the picture below?

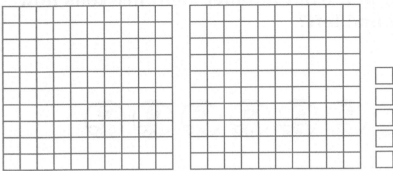

- ○ 250
- ● 205
- ○ 52
- ○ 25

10   In the number 4,067 which place holds a zero?

- ○ ones
- ○ tens
- ● hundreds
- ○ thousands

11   Use the centimeter side of your ruler. What is the length of the figure's longest side?

5 the longer on

- ● 5 centimeters
- ○ 4 centimeters
- ○ 3 centimeters
- ○ 2 centimeters

12 Which figure comes next in the pattern?

● □ ○ ■ ● □ ○ ■ ●

○   ●

◐   □

○   ○

○   ■

13 Which would you use to measure weight?

○ inch

○ cup

○ kilometer

◉ pound

14 Steven has to choose the number he thinks the spinner will land on. Which number should he choose?

◉ 1

○ 2

◐ 3

○ 4

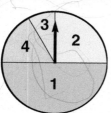

15 Janet has two coins in her pocket. Which amount could she **not** have?

◐ 26 cents

○ 20 cents

○ 15 cents

◉ 7 cents

Go ▶

16 Which number is the same as eight thousand six hundred forty?

- ○ 864
- ○ 8,064
- ○ 8,604
- ● 8,640

17 Which number sentence has an answer smaller than 10?

- ○ $10 - 0 =$ ___
- ● $10 - 5 =$ ___
- ○ $10 + 0 =$ ___
- ○ $10 + 5 =$ ___

18 Look at the clock. How many minutes are there until 6:00?

- ○ 9 minutes
- ○ 25 minutes
- ● 45 minutes
- ○ 1 hour

19 What is the shape of the street sign?

- ○ circle
- ○ square
- ● rectangle
- ○ triangle

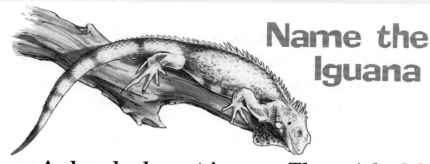

Name the Iguana

Directions: A class had a pet iguana. They picked four names. Then everyone picked the name they liked best. What they picked is shown in the graph below. Use the graph to answer problems 20 through 22.

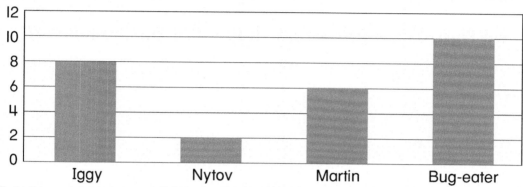

20 Which name was chosen by the most students?

- ○ Iggy
- ○ Nytov
- ○ Martin
- ◉ Bug-eater

21 How many more students chose Martin than chose Nytov?

- ○ 2
- ◉ 4
- ○ 6
- ○ 8

22 The next day three students who picked Bug-eater changed their mind. They decided they liked Nytov better. What is the winning name now?

- ◉ Iggy
- ○ Nytov
- ○ Martin
- ○ Bug-eater

23 On her way to school, Dana found three pennies near her house. Then she found five nickels at the bus stop. On the bus she found a quarter and a dime. How would you find the number of coins she found in all?

- ● add
- ○ divide
- ○ multiply
- ○ subtract

24 Which two figures are the same shape and the same size?

| 1 | 2 | 3 |

| 4 | 5 | 6 |

- ○ 1 and 5
- ● 2 and 6
- ○ 2 and 4
- ○ 2 and 3

25 Kyle's dog, Barkum, is 6 years old. If he were a person, how old would he be? Follow the directions below.

A Dog's Age

1. Find how old your dog is.

2. Multiply the number of years by 7.

3. The answer is your dog's age if he were a person.

- ○ 13 years old
- ○ 35 years old
- ● 42 years old
- ○ 49 years old

Sample A

Mary has 6 uncles and 9 aunts. How many uncles and aunts does she have in all?

- ○ 13
- ○ 14
- ● 15
- ○ 16
- ○ None of these

Sample B

Use the inch side of your ruler to solve this problem.

How many inches long is the pencil?

- ○ 7 inches
- ● 6 inches
- ○ 5 inches
- ○ 4 inches

STOP

1 **4 x 9 =**

○ 13
○ 27
◉ 36
○ 49
○ None of these

2 **78 – 5 =**

◉ 73
○ 74
○ 28
○ 83
○ None of these

3 **48 ÷ 6 =**

○ 54
○ 42
○ 7
○ 9
◉ None of these

4 **2.7 + 0.6 =**

○ 2.3
○ 2.76
○ 2.13
◉ 3.3
○ None of these

5 **674**
   + 228

○ 802
○ 892
◉ 902
○ 992
○ None of these

6 **559**
   – 523

○ 536
○ 26
◉ 36
◉ 63
○ None of these

7   **10**
   x 10

◉ 100
○ 20
○ 1,000
○ 1,010
○ None of these

8 What number goes in the box to make the number sentence true?

$$6 + \square = 15$$

- ○ 21
- ○ 19
- ○ 11
- ● 9

9 What number sentence tells how many brothers Kim and Tara have in all?

> Tara has five brothers.
> Kim has three brothers.

- ○ $5 + 3 = 2$
- ● $5 + 3 = 8$
- ○ $5 - 3 = 2$
- ○ $5 - 3 = 8$

10 Hope bought two stamps. The total cost was 55 cents. She used a dollar. How much change did she get?

- ○ 55 cents
- ● 45 cents
- ○ 35 cents
- ○ one dollar and 55 cents

11 Which number is the same as three thousand five hundred six?

- ○ 356
- ○ 3,560
- ○ 30,506
- ● 3,506

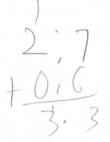

12 What number is shown by the blocks in the picture below?

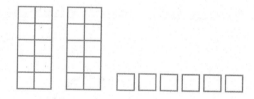

- ○ 206
- ○ 62
- ● 26
- ○ 602

13 Which shape has exactly three sides?

- ● triangle
- ○ square
- ○ rectangle
- ○ circle

Directions: Use estimation to find the best answers for problems 14 and 15.

14 Which number is closest to 213 + 480?

- ○ 500
- ◉ 600
- ● 700
- ○ 800

15 Suppose you pay for the two items below using a $20 bill. About how much change will you receive?

- ◉ $11
- ○ $9
- ○ $8
- ● $7

$7.99 $4.99

16 Look at the pattern below. What number comes next?

- ● 35
- ○ 40
- ○ 55
- ○ 60

15, 20, 25, 30, ___

17 Daniel wrote numbers on the slips of paper shown below. He picks one slip of paper. What number will most likely show up?

- ◉ 1
- ○ 2
- ● 3
- ○ 4

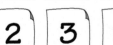

1	1	2	2
2	3	3	3
3	4	4	

18 Mike's Collectibles and Comics has this sign posted on its door.

MIKE'S

Hours

Monday — Friday
10AM — 5PM

Saturday
9AM — 4PM

Kiera wants to get to Mike's on Saturday as soon as it opens. It takes her 30 minutes to walk there from home. When should she leave her home?

- ● 8:30 A.M.
- ○ 9:00 A.M.
- ○ 9:30 A.M.
- ○ 10:30 A.M.

19 What number goes in the box to make the number sentence true?

$$9 - \square = 3$$

- ○ 3
- ● 6
- ○ 12
- ○ 27

20 There was a baseball game last night. There were 32,085 fans. Which number is in the thousands place of 32,085?

- ○ 3
- ● 2
- ○ 0
- ○ 8

21 Which number in the box is greatest?

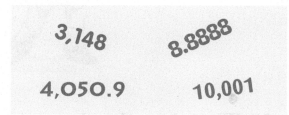

3,148   8.8888

4,050.9   10,001

- ○ 3,148
- ● 10,001
- ○ 4,050.9
- ○ 8.8888

22 What shape appears next in the pattern?

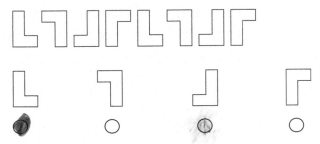

○   ○   ○   ○

23 The minute hand on a clock moved from the 3 to the 7.
How many minutes passed?

● 20 minutes

○ 15 minutes

○ 10 minutes

○ 4 minutes

24 Iris has more brothers than sisters. She has 10 brothers
and sisters in all. How many sisters could she have?

○ 7

○ 6

○ 5

● 4

25 What does the sign <u>not</u> tell you?

○ the price for a woman's haircut

○ the price for a boy's haircut

○ the time the store closes on Wednesday

● the special price for kids under 3 years old

Caroline's Haircuts

Prices
Men and Women $12.00
Boys and Girls $8.00

Hours
Monday–Saturday
7am–7pm
Closed Sunday

26 **Bonnie walked from the park to school. How could she walk?**

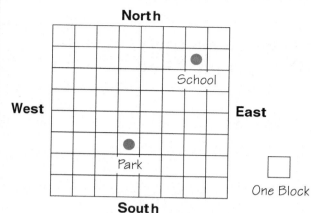

North

West   East

School

Park

South

One Block

○ go 3 blocks west and 5 blocks south

● go 4 blocks north and 3 blocks east

○ go 3 blocks east and 5 blocks north

○ go 5 blocks south and 3 blocks west

27 **Use the inch side of your ruler. Which figure is 1 inch wide?**

○   ○   ●   ○

28 **Veronica wrote a capital letter V on a sheet of paper. She turned it upside down. It looked very different. Which letter looks the same when it is turned upside down?**

○ capital letter F

○ capital letter G

● capital letter H

○ capital letter J

OUR FAVORITE COLORS

Directions: The students in a third-grade class chose their favorite colors. The graph shows the results. Read the graph. Then use it to answer problems 29 through 31.

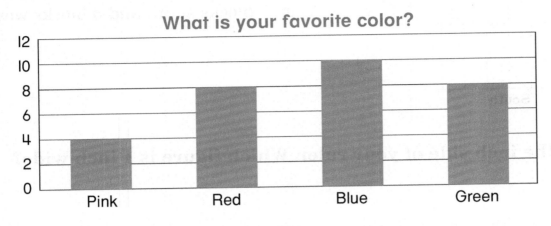

What is your favorite color?

29 **How many students chose Blue?**

- ● 10
- ○ 8
- ○ 5
- ○ 4

30 **Which two colors were chosen by the same number of students?**

- ○ Pink and Red
- ● Red and Green
- ○ Red and Blue
- ○ Green and Blue

31 **Two girls picked Red. How many boys picked Red?**

- ○ 2
- ○ 4
- ○ 6
- ● 8

32 Which shape is different from the rest?

○

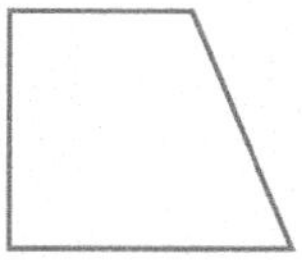

○

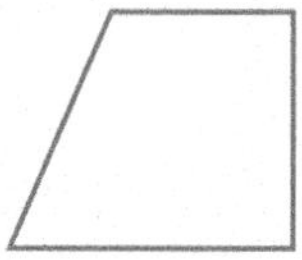

●

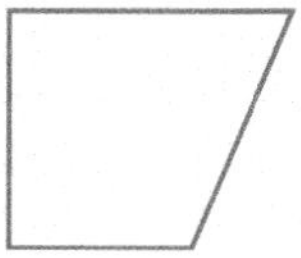

○

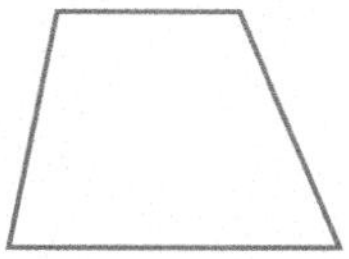

33 Which fraction of the square is shaded?

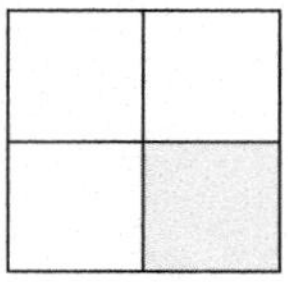

○ $\frac{1}{3}$

● $\frac{1}{4}$

○ $\frac{2}{3}$

○ $\frac{3}{4}$

34 August 1 was a Monday. What day of the week was August 31?

◐ Monday

● Wednesday

○ Friday

○ Sunday

Go

35 **What number is missing in the pattern?**

8, 12, 16, ___, 24, ...

- ○ 17
- ○ 18
- ○ 19
- ● 20

36 **Which is most likely measured in pounds?**

- ○ the height of a building
- ○ the depth of an ocean
- ● the weight of a piano
- ○ the weight of a feather

37 **Mr. Forbes made dinner last night. He cooked for his wife, himself, their six children, and four friends. How many dinners did Mr. Forbes make?**

- ○ 10
- ○ 11
- ● 12
- ○ 13

38 **A calculator showed the number below. What number is one greater?**

- ● four thousand five hundred sixty
- ○ four thousand five hundred six
- ○ four thousand six hundred
- ○ four thousand six hundred sixty

39 A girl spins the spinner. Where will it most likely land after the spin?

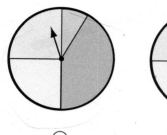 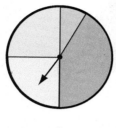 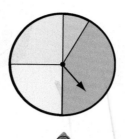 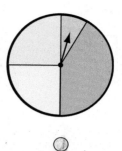

    ○   ○   ●   ◐

40 Georgia has an odd number of dimes in her pocket. How much money could she have in dimes?

    ○ $1.00
    ○ $0.77
    ● $0.60
    ○ $0.50

41 How many small triangles will there be in the next picture of the pattern?

 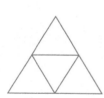 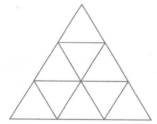

    ○ 16
    ○ 15
    ○ 14
    ● 12

42 Which tool measures weight?

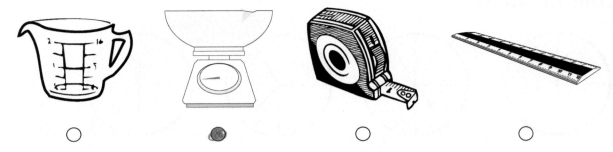

○   ●   ○   ○

43 Ling is using these counters to solve a number sentence. Which number sentence could it be?

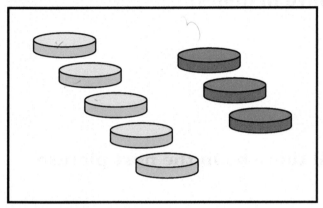

● 5 x 3 = 15
○ 5 + 3 = 8
○ 5 − 3 = 2
○ 3 − 5 = 2

44 Billy bought 1 comic book on Monday. He bought 2 comic books on Tuesday, and 3 comic books on Wednesday. Billy continues this pattern. How many comic books will he own by the end of Saturday?

● 6
○ 11
○ 15
○ 21

SPORTS TIME

Directions: Riddel Beach School held sports sign-up day.
Use the direction sign to answer problems 45 through 47.

45 **What is the shape of the sign called?**

- ○ rectangle
- ○ pentagon
- ○ hexagon
- ◉ octagon

<table>
<tr><td colspan="2" align="center">Sports Teams
Sign-Up Day</td></tr>
<tr><td align="center">Last Name
begins with</td><td align="center">Go to
Room</td></tr>
<tr><td align="center">A-F</td><td align="center">107</td></tr>
<tr><td align="center">G-M</td><td align="center">121</td></tr>
<tr><td align="center">N-S</td><td align="center">214</td></tr>
<tr><td align="center">T-Z</td><td align="center">216</td></tr>
</table>

46 **Andrea Punzalan wants to sign up for soccer. Where should she go?**

- ◉ Room 107
- ○ Room 121
- ○ Room 214
- ○ Room 216

47 **Ninety students want to sign up for soccer. Sixty want to sign up for baseball. One-third of those students go to room 214. How many students is that?**

- ○ 20
- ◉ 30
- ○ 40
- ○ 50

Directions: Elections were held for third-grade president. The chart shows the results. Use the chart to answer problems 48 through 50.

Kiyo	⳽⳽⳽⳽⳽ |
Darren	⳽⳽⳽⳽⳽ ⳽⳽⳽⳽⳽
Robert	||||
Samantha	⳽⳽⳽⳽⳽ ⳽⳽⳽⳽⳽ ||
Vishnu	⳽⳽⳽⳽⳽ ||||

48 Who won the election?

- ○ Kiyo
- ○ Darren
- ○ Samantha
- ○ Vishnu

49 How many votes did Kiyo receive?

- ○ 11
- ○ 7
- ○ 6
- ○ 5

Vote for Kiyo

50 What is not on the chart?

- ○ how many students voted
- ○ who got the fewest number of votes
- ○ who came in second place
- ○ when the voting took place

Answer Key

Reading

Lesson 1-page 8

SA	They do not want to hurt Mom's feelings.
SB	playing hide-and-seek
1.	in the mountains
2.	The path was dangerous.
3.	She feeds him the food he likes.
4.	girl and donkey
5.	She would take care of him.
6.	careless
7.	They did not want to share the mouse.
8.	She does not want them to fight.
9.	You should not fight.
10.	It ran away when the kittens started to fight.

Reading Review Test

page 14

SA	two weeks
1.	a den
2.	at home
3.	thoughts
4.	a dreamer
5.	She would fix the rip.
6.	He didn't listen to his mother.
7.	Sneezy Snatcher was huge.
8.	happy
9.	She let Sammy go home to get the pudding.
10.	The name Appleseed tells you what he did.
11.	was a very special person
12.	acts to help others
13.	was born in Massachusetts
14.	a child who wants a dog
15.	to walk and feed the dog
16.	it's not all right
17.	Make her believe you.

Language Arts

Lesson 2-page 24

SA	is my best friend
SB	more interesting
1.	write
2.	Dear Maria,
3.	Your cousin,
4.	work at it
5.	Brenda and her mom

Lesson 3-page 26

SA	It is where I do my homework.
SB	Cindy helps her father with the housework.
1.	Ned is a hard worker.
2.	I like to read fairy tales the best. I dream I'm a queen.
3.	Michael lives on a farm.
4.	After a tree is cut down, you can see rings on the stump.

Lesson 4-page 28

SA	My sister and I play together.
SB	I didn't want the bird to stop.
1.	They
2.	Flying through the air is fun.
3.	The rain rolled down the roof.
4.	She likes to sit in her old chair.
5.	You would not see a bear on the streets of New York City.

Language Arts Review Test

page 30

SA	sang
1.	A baker
2.	like
3.	before

4. His life was never very easy.

5. He started to work before he was eight years old.

6. One day he opened a clothing store.

7. Soon he had many stores.

8. Kristi worked hard to be a winner.

9. The ice is very slippery.

10. Music is played.

11. skater

12. Dear Carol,

13. Your friend,

Reading and Language Arts Comprehensive Test

page 37

SA to school

SB is old

1. in his bed

2. The boy has a set of toy ships.

3. sick

4. The toys are real things.

5. stay

6. climb the hills

7. He

8. Edward needed a baby sitter

9. to keep him from flying away

10. a chicken

11. Edward spoke to her.

12. jumped

13. awful

14. She wanted to have him for lunch.

15. staring

16. They were put into a box.

17. They got smelly.

18. He was nervous.

19. He thinks Irwin brings good luck.

20. Irwin did not like being worn for sports.

21. thankful because he's still useful

22. Andres and Anna

23. gloves

24. wear

25. light

26. They hoped to get money.

27. selfish and cruel

28. He was afraid the townsfolk would hurt him.

29. He gave them what they wanted.

30. The dragon helped the townsfolk.

31. You should be kind to others.

32. Those townsfolk were angry.

33. nicer

34. rules the country

35. It is hard to be a good king.

36. hatter's

37. wig

38. back

39. news

40. because he was a home run hitter

41. They were the first African–Americans to play major league baseball.

42. He was one of the first black men to play major league baseball.

43. happy because people remembered what he did

44. honor

45. He grew up to become a home run champ. He helped the Cleveland Indians win the World Series in 1948.

46. You play stickball with a stick.

47. The two top teams play each other.

48. party

49. best

50. Dear Jane,

51. Your cousin,

52. She worked in a cotton mill in the 1850s.

53. A cotton mill was a place where they made cloth.

54. After that Matty invented a new machine that was safer.

55. She was only 12 years old when she invented the machine.

56. she did not want to bore her friends

57. well–known

58. She wanted to stay friends with them.

59. that is the life she knows

60. She grew up in California.

61. practice

62. While

63. My mother bought me all the books I loved.

64. Amy always loved to read.

65. Today she lives in San Francisco.

66. They visited China together.

67. You can write on a computer.

68. She loves reading.

69. The poet

70. I sit at my desk and think. Then I write little stories.

Lesson 1 - page 71

S   306
1.   47
2.   140

Lesson 2 - page 72

S   31
1.   None of these
2. $20

Lesson 3 - page 73

S   8
1.   13
2.   40 + 30 = 70

Lesson 4 - page 74

S   25 minutes
1.   6 cm
2.   the width of a photo

Lesson 5 - page 75

S

1.   S and U
2.   square

Lesson 6 - page 76

S   4
1.   10 students
2.   24

Lesson 7 - page 77

S   120
1.   16
2.   May 25

Lesson 8 - page 78

S $1.00
1.   25 days
2.   14 cents

Lesson 9 - page 79

S $14
1.   92 miles
2.   at the park

page 80

1.   45
2.   None of these
3.   63
4. $1.34
5.   7 - 3 = 4
6.   box of cookies
7.   700
8.   200
9.   205
10.   hundreds
11.   5 centimeters
12.   ☐
13.   pound
14.   1
15.   7 cents
16.   8,640
17.   10 - 5 = __
18.   45 minutes
19.   rectangle
20.   Bug-eater
21.   4
22.   Iggy
23.   add
24.   2 and 6
25.   42 years old

page 87

SA   15

SB   6 inches

Part 1 - page 88

1.   36

2.   73

3.   None of these

4.   3.3

5.   902

6.   36

7.   100

8.   9

9. $5 + 3 = 8$

10.   45 cents

11.   3,506

12.   26

13.   triangle

Part 2 - page 90

14.   700

15. $7

16.   35

17.   3

18.   8:30 A.M.

19.   6

20.   2

21.   10,001

22.

23.   20 minutes

24.   4

25.   the special price for kids under 3 years old

26.   go 4 blocks north and 3 blocks east

27.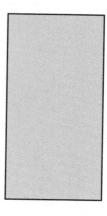

28.   capital letter H

29.   10

30.   Red and Green

31.   6

32.

33. $\frac{1}{4}$

34.   Wednesday

35.   20

36.   the weight of a piano

37.   12

38.   four thousand five hundred sixty

39.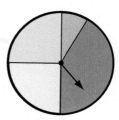

40. $0.50

41.   16

42.

43. 5 + 3 = 8

44. 21

45. octagon

46. Room 214

47. 50

48. Samantha

49. 6

50. when the voting took place